Book 1

MENTAL
MATH
WORKOUTS

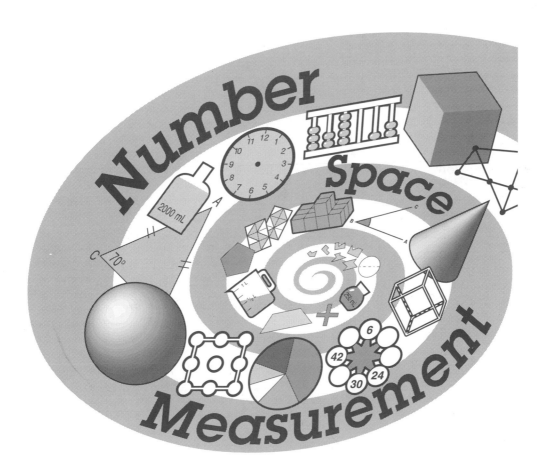

Written by George Moore

World Teachers Press

Order Number 2-5046
ISBN 1-885111-60-6

F   01

Educational Resources

395 Main Street
Rowley, MA 01969

Mental Math Workouts

Foreword

MENTAL MATH WORKOUTS present mental mathematical problems in a challenging worksheet format. Each book contains 24 reproducible worksheets, with almost 200 different types of mental math problems, based on curriculum concepts in number, space and measurement. The format emphasizes problem solving and mathematical facts.

Each **MENTAL MATH WORKOUTS** book contains 12 worksheet sets and 12 review sets. The worksheet sets cover a wide variety of mental mathematical problems from across the curriculum. The revision sets provide similar kinds of problems to their corresponding worksheets, with a slightly greater degree of difficulty, to reinforce the mathematical concepts covered. It is recommended that the revision sets be used after general class difficulties have been treated, to both reinforce math facts and assess each student's progress in learning math.

A glossary of math terms and student assessment record are included in this book. The glossary provides a reference for the teacher and students to the math language used throughout the series. The assessment record provides the teacher with a single record sheet for keeping track of each student's progress through the worksheets and review sheets, with space provided to note the weakness areas of the class which may require reinforcement.

Contents

About the author:
George Moore has been a practicing classroom teacher for over 30 years, with experience in primary and secondary areas. He has held teaching and promotional positions in England, New South Wales and Western Australia.

Mental Math Workouts

Introduction

Mental calculation in mathematics is an essential part of skill development in primary schools. The ability to mentally calculate and solve problems allows students to cope with more complex mathematical concepts in later years and more importantly provides a life skill that is constantly used in daily life.

The activities in this book provide coverage of all areas of mathematics including number, space, measurement and handling data and have a strong problem-solving component. Mental calculation should be seen as an area of significant skill focus where students need to be taught the skills of mental calculation rather than simply complete multiple examples of simple basic facts. Each set of activities in this series is reinforced later in the book with further activities of an identical nature. This allows for consolidation for the student and provides an opportunity for teachers to evaluate the progress of individual students.

Calculators

Calculators are a tool of mathematics as computers are also seen as a tool in education. It is the philosophy of the author that students need to develop the skills of functional calculator use but the calculator should not replace the need for developing mental calculation skills. Activities in this book require calculator usage in specified situations that are intended to develop the skills of calculator usage and should not be used for other problems which require a mental calculation.

Calculators can be used as a marking tool in some situations.

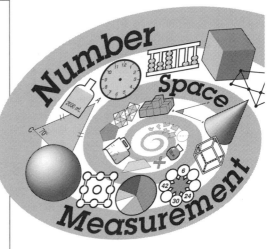

Answers

Answers are provided at the back of this book. The process of marking work in this form of activity is an essential part of the learning program. It is during this process that individual and group problems can be identified and either discussed or become part of future math programs. A recording sheet is provided so that individual student progress can be monitored throughout the use of these activities.

Basic Facts

The activities in this book are not intended to replace the work involved in mathematical basic facts such as tables and instant recall. This form of work should be ongoing and will compliment students' abilities to complete this form of mental calculation.

Mental Math Workouts · Example Lesson Development

The following is a lesson development using one of the pages in this book. It is an example of how the activity could be introduced, developed and extended.

Activity   Set 1 - page 10

Introductory Work

It is suggested that introductory activities for all of the activities in this book can be selected from the following strategies:

- Basic fact and table work which focuses on speed of recall and will encourage students to focus on their mental calculation process. These types of activities can vary from simple games and competitions to more formal drills.
- Review the previous set and discuss and complete examples that may have caused difficulty.
- Each lesson, select a different problem that can be found on the worksheets to focus on and demonstrate various methods to gain a solution.

Oral work can at times be threatening to individual students no matter what their skill level. Therefore teachers should be aware that the activities are enjoyable, non-threatening in their nature and encourage participation and accept the chance of error.

Completing the Worksheets

The following is a suggestion for the development of this activity.

1. Encourage students to read instructions for each question thoroughly. It is vital that a complete understanding of what is required is gained before any strategies are applied.

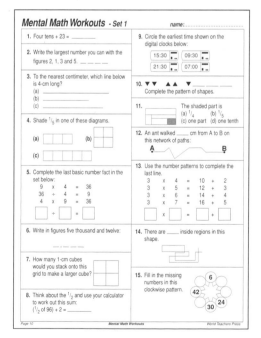

2. Answers should be clearly written. The emphasis is on mental calculation and accuracy rather than speed.

3. Use of the "Glossary of Terms" is an important part of this program. Students may be given access to these sheets to assist with understanding of the questions.

4. Measurement activities may be affected by photocopying of these worksheets and should be taken into account.

Extension

It is important that areas of weakness in both the individual and the whole class are identified and included in future teaching programs. Corresponding revision lists are provided which reinforce similar concepts at a slightly more difficult level.

acute: describes an angle between 0° and 90°.

adjacent: adjoining (as used to describe lines and angles).

alternate: every other one in a sequence.

angle: the number of degrees rotated around a point.

arc: part of the circumference of a circle.

area: the amount of space within a perimeter (expressed in square units).

arithmetic mean: the average of a set of numbers.

array: the arrangement of the units of a number in rows and columns (e.g. 6 = : : :).

ascending order: the arrangement of numbers from smallest to largest.

average: a number representing a set of numbers (obtained by dividing the total of the numbers by the number of numbers in the set).

axis (of symmetry): a line dividing a shape into two symmetrical parts.

bar graph: a diagram representing information by the length of bars.

base: the line or face on which a shape is standing.

base angles: those angles adjacent to the base of a shape.

block graph: a diagram representing information by the length of blocks.

capacity: the amount of space in the interior of an object (the amount of liquid/air it contains).

Carroll diagram: a problem-solving diagram used in classification activities.

chord: a straight line connecting two points on the circumference of a circle.

chronological: describes dates arranged in the order in which they occur (e.g. 1920, 1936, 1992, etc.).

circumference: the distance around a circle (its perimeter).

clockwise: moving in the same direction as the hands of a clock.

closed curve: a curve which has no end points.

common numeral: the symbol commonly used to represent a math expression (e.g. the common numeral for 10^3 is 1,000).

composite number: a number with more than two factors.

concentric circles: circles which have the same center point.

congruent: congruent shapes are the same shape and size (equal).

consecutive: consecutive numbers follow in order without interruption (e.g. 11, 12, 13, 14).

coordinates: numbers used to locate a point on a grid.

counter-clockwise: moving in the opposite direction to the hand on a clock.

cubed: a cubed number is the answer when the square of a number is multiplied by the number itself.

cylinder: a circular prism with two congruent, parallel circular end-faces.

denominator: the number below the line in a fraction.

descending order: the arrangement of numbers from largest to smallest.

diagonal: a straight line connecting two non-adjacent vertices (corners) of a polygon.

diameter: a straight line connecting two points on the circumference of a circle and passing through the circle's center.

difference: by how much a number is bigger or smaller than another.

digit: any number from 0 to 9 (inclusive).

digital clock: a clock that shows the time by using numbers rather than hands.

dimensions: the measurements of a shape (i.e. length, width, height).

doubling: multiplying a number or shape by two.

edge: the intersection of two faces of a three-dimensional object.

equation: a statement of equality between two expressions (e.g. 3 x 4 = 6 + 6).

equilateral triangle: a triangle with congruent (equal) sides and angles.

equivalent: having the same value.

even number: a positive (8) or negative (–6) number exactly divisible by two.

face: a plane surface of a three-dimensional object.

face value: the numeral itself despite its position in a number (e.g. the face value of the 5 in 3520 is 5).

factor: a number which will divide exactly into another number.

factorial: the product of all the numbers from 1 to a given number (e.g. the factorial of 4 is 1 x 2 x 3 x 4 = 24).

Fibonacci numbers: a series of numbers in which any number is the sum of the previous two.

fraction: an amount expressed in terms of a numerator and a denominator (usually part of a whole).

heptagon: a two-dimensional shape with seven sides and seven angles.

hexagon: a polygon with six sides and six angles.

hexagonal: having the shape of a hexagon.

hexahedron: a three-dimensional shape with six faces.

horizontal: describes a line or plane parallel to the earth's surface.

improper fraction: a fraction whose numerator is equal to or greater than its denominator.

index notation: a short way of writing large numbers by multiplication of repeated factors.

integer: a negative or positive whole number (e.g. … −2, −1, 0, 1, 2 …).

interior angles: the angles inside a shape.

intersection: the point or line where two lines or two faces meet or in set theory, those elements common to two or more sets.

irregular shapes: shapes which do not have all congruent sides and all congruent angles.

isosceles triangle: a triangle with two congruent sides and two congruent angles.

line graph: a diagram using straight lines to join points representing certain information.

line segment: a line with two end points.

mapping diagram: a diagram showing the relationship between sets of information by using arrows.

mass: the amount of matter in an object (its weight on earth).

mean (arithmetic mean): the average of a set of numbers.

median: in statistics, the middle measurement when information is arranged in order of size (e.g. 5 is the median of 2, 3, 5, 10, 13). Where there is no middle score, an average of the two central scores is taken.

mixed numeral: a symbol representing a whole number and a fraction (e.g. $2\frac{3}{8}$).

modal score: in statistics, the measurement that occurs most often. (e.g. the modal score of 2, 7, 4, 4, 3, 4, 9, 4 is 4).

multiples: the multiples of a number are those numbers which a given number will divide into exactly (e.g. some multiples of 3 are 3, 12, 21, 60, etc.).

net: a flat pattern that can be folded to make a three-dimensional model of a shape.

network: a system of lines (paths) and nodes (points representing intersections).

numeral: a symbol used to represent a number (e.g. 5 and V are numerals representing the number 5).

numerator: the number above the line in a fraction.

obtuse angle: an angle between 90° and 180°.

octagon: a polygon with eight sides and eight angles.

octahedron: a polyhedron (three-dimensional shape) with eight faces.

odd number: a number that when divided by two leaves a remainder of one.

parallel lines: lines with no common points and always the same distance apart.

parallelogram: a four-sided polygon with opposite sides equal and parallel and containing no right angles.

path: a line connecting nodes (points) in a network.

pentagon: a polygon with five sides and five angles.

pentomino: a plane shape made of five congruent squares connected to each other by at least one common side.

percentage: a quantity expressed in hundredths.

perfect number: a number which is the sum of its factors excluding itself (e.g. 6 = 1 + 2 + 3).

perimeter: the length of the distance around the boundary of a shape.

perpendicular line: a line at right angles to another line or plane.

pie graph: a circular graph in which sectors of a circle are used to show information.

place value: indicates the position of a numeral (e.g. the place value of the 3 in the number 357 is hundreds).

polygon: a two-dimensional shape with three or more straight lines.

polyhedron (plural – polyhedra): a three-dimensional shape with plane faces.

prime factor: a prime number that will divide exactly into another number (e.g. 2 and 3 are prime factors of 6).

prime number: a number with only two factors, 1 and itself.

prism: a three-dimensional shape with at least one pair of opposite faces which are congruent and parallel.

product: the result when two or more numbers are multiplied (e.g. the product of 2, 3, 4 is 2 x 3 x 4 = 24).

proper fraction (vulgar fraction): a fraction in which the numerator is less than the denominator.

property: an attribute of a two-dimensional or three-dimensional shape.

protractor: a semi-circular or circular instrument for measuring angles.

pyramid: a three-dimensional shape with a square base and four sloping triangular sides meeting at a common vertex.

quadrant: a quarter of the area of a circle which also contains a right angle.

quadrilateral: any four-sided polygon.

radius: a line joining the center of a circle to a point on the circle's circumference.

rectangle: a quadrilateral with opposite sides equal and parallel and containing four right angles (a square is a rectangle).

reflex angle: an angle greater than 180°.

region: the interior area enclosed by a perimeter (the area outside the perimeter is the exterior region).

regular shape: a polygon is regular if all its sides and angles are congruent (opposite – irregular).

rhombus: a parallelogram with congruent sides and containing no right angles (a diamond shape).

right angle: an angle containing 90°.

right-angled triangle: a triangle containing one right angle (90°).

rotating: turning in a clockwise or counter-clockwise direction.

scalene triangle: a triangle with sides of different length and three different interior angles.

sector: the part of a circle bounded by two radii and the included arc.

segment: the part of a circle bounded by a chord and an arc.

semicircle: half a circle (the area bounded by a diameter and an arc).

similar shapes: have the same shape but differ in size.

simplify: to change to simpler terms (e.g. $^{45}/_{60}$ to $^{3}/_{4}$)

solid shape: a three-dimensional shape (with length, width, height).

sphere: a three-dimensional shape comprising a set of points, each point being equidistant from its center (e.g. a ball).

squared: a number squared is multiplied by itself.

square number: a number whose units can be arranged into a square (e.g. 4 : :).

sum: the result when two or more numbers are added.

supplementary angles: two angles which, when added, total 180°.

surface area: the total area of all faces of a three-dimensional shape.

symmetrical: a shape is symmetrical if it is identical on either side of a line dividing it into two parts.

tally: a record of items using vertical and oblique lines to represent each item.

tessellating shapes: shapes which cover an area with no gaps between them.

tetrahedron: a polyhedron with four faces (e.g. triangular pyramid).

tetromino: a plane shape made of four congruent squares connected to each other by at least one common side.

three (3-) dimensional shape: a shape with length, width and height.

total: the result when two or more numbers are added.

total value: what quantity a numeral represents according to its position (in 'tens', 'hundreds' column etc.).

trapezium: a quadrilateral with two parallel sides.

traversable: a network is traversable if it can be traced over without going over the same path twice.

triangular number: a number whose units can be arranged into a triangle (e.g. 6).

tromino: a plane shape made of three congruent squares connected to each other by at least one common side.

twin primes: prime numbers separated by a composite number (e.g. **3**, 4, **5**).

Venn diagram: a diagram which shows sets and their relationships.

vertex (plural – vertices): the point at which two or more line segments or two or more edges of a polyhedron meet.

vertical line: a line which is at right angles to a horizontal line.

volume: the amount of space taken up by an object.

Symbols Used

>	greater than
=	is equal to
≈	is approximately equal to
<	less than
≠	is not equal to

Mental Math Workouts

Student Name	Work Sets 1 – 12												Review Sets 1 – 12											
	1	2	3	4	5	6	7	8	9	10	11	12	1	2	3	4	5	6	7	8	9	10	11	12

Class: **Record sheet**   **of**

Weak areas in work sets to be reinforced before review sets are done:

1. _____
2. _____
3. _____
4. _____
5. _____
6. _____
7. _____
8. _____
9. _____
10. _____
11. _____
12. _____

Weaknesses are readily diagnosed by a show of hands for errors.

Mental Math Workouts - Set 1

name:......................

1. Four tens + 23 = _____

2. Write the largest number you can with the figures 2, 1, 3 and 5. ___ ___ ___ ___

3. To the nearest centimeter, which line below is 4-cm long?

(a) _____

(b) _____

(c) _____

4. Shade $\frac{1}{5}$ in one of these diagrams.

(a) [diagram]   (b) [diagram]

(c) [diagram]

5. Complete the last basic number fact in the set below:

```
 9   x   4   =   36
36   ÷   4   =    9
 4   x   9   =   36
```

[ ] ÷ [ ] = [ ]

6. Write the number five thousand and twelve:

___ , ___ ___ ___

7. How many 1-cm cubes would you stack onto this grid to make a larger cube?

8. Think about the $\frac{1}{2}$ and use your calculator to work out this sum:

($\frac{1}{2}$ of 96) + 2 = _____

9. Circle the earliest time shown on the digital clocks below:

15:30   09:30

21:30   07:00

10. ▼ ▼ ☐ ▲ ▲ ☐ ▼ ___ ___ ___
Complete the pattern of shapes.

11.  The shaded part is
(a) $\frac{1}{4}$ (b) $\frac{1}{5}$
(c) one part   (d) one tenth

12. An ant walked _____ cm from A to B on this network of paths:

A _____ **B**

13. Use the number patterns to complete the last line.

```
3   x   4   =   10   +   2
3   x   5   =   12   +   3
3   x   6   =   14   +   4
3   x   7   =   16   +   5
```

[ ] x [ ] = [ ] + [ ]

14. There are _____ inside regions in this shape.

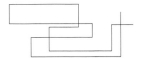

15. Fill in the missing numbers in this clockwise pattern.

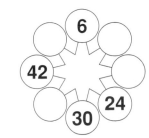

Mental Math Workouts - Set 2

name:....................

1. ☐ ÷ 4 = 5

2. I estimate the width of our classroom is
   _____ meters.

3. 37 rounded to the nearest 10 = _____ .

4. Toffees are 5¢ each but if I buy a
   packet of ten for 35¢ I save myself
   _____ cents.

5. 5 x ☐ = 3 x 10

6. When zero is subtracted from a number the
   answer is always:
   (a) a zero, (b) one, (c) less than the number,
   (d) the same as the number.

7. This shape is divided into:
   (a) thirds
   (b) equal parts
   (c) 3 unequal parts
   (d) quarters
   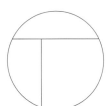

8. XXIV – XVIII = _____
   Give the answer in Roman numerals.

9.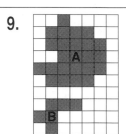
   The area of shape A is:
   (a) 2 x shape B's area.
   (b) 3 x shape B's area.
   (c) 4 x shape B's area.
   (d) 6 x shape B's area.

10. A   B
    Shape A = 7 intersections
    Shape B = _____
    intersections

11.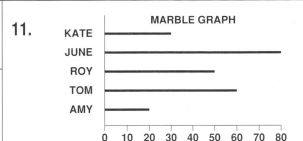
    MARBLE GRAPH
    KATE
    JUNE
    ROY
    TOM
    AMY
    0 10 20 30 40 50 60 70 80

    Tom has _____ times as many marbles
    as Amy but only 10 more than _____ on
    this bar graph.

12. These are two arrays for the number 6. Draw
    two arrays for the number 4 below:
    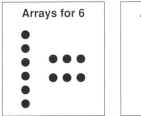

    | Arrays for 6 | Arrays for 4 |

13.
    diameter
    The diameter of a circle is
    twice its radius. The
    radius of this circle is
    _____ mm
    (use a ruler).

14. This cube has
    ☐ faces and
    ☐ edges

15.
    halves
    quarters

    This diagram shows that the fraction $\frac{1}{2}$ is

    the same as the fraction ☐ .

Mental Math Workouts - Set 3

name:.....................

1. Shade the multiples of 3.

3	4	5	6	7	8	9	10	11	12

2. If you halve an even number the answer is:
- (a) always odd
- (b) always even
- (c) odd or even
- (d) not odd or even

3. 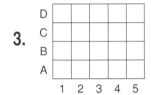 Put an X in grid square (2,C) and color in grid square (4,A).

4. Use the halving and doubling pattern to find the missing numbers:

$$40 \times 10 = 400$$
$$20 \times 20 = 400$$
$$10 \times 40 = 400$$
$$\boxed{} \times \boxed{} = 400$$

5. 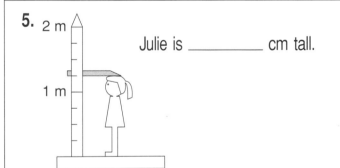 Julie is _____ cm tall.

6. Complete the last 2 shapes in this repeating pattern.

7. 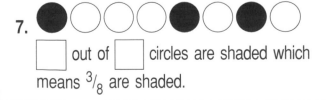 ⬤◯◯◯⬤◯⬤◯

☐ out of ☐ circles are shaded which means $\frac{3}{8}$ are shaded.

8. This is a closed curve with one intersection. Draw a closed curve with 2 intersections in the box.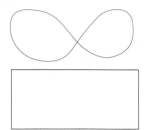

9. Draw a line twice as long as line 'A' and then divide the new line into 4 equal lengths (ruler needed).   **A** ———

10. I throw two dice and a 6 and a 3 come up. My next throw will be:
- (a) a 6 and a 3   (b) two 6's
- (c) I can't tell   (d) two 3's.

11. 400 + 27 units =

H	**T**	**U**

12. △ x ☐ x △ = 24

The missing number in the square is 3 times the number in the triangles.

13.

8	1	6
3		
4		2

Use the addition pattern to complete the missing numbers.

14. Join 2 points on the parallel sides and divide the trapezium into 2 congruent (equal) shapes (ruler needed).

15. Concentric circles have the same center. The width of the second largest concentric circle shown is _____ mm.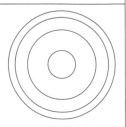

Mental Math Workouts - Set 4

name:......................

1. The answer to an even number multiplied by an even number:
(a) is always odd (c) is always even
(b) is odd or even (d) always ends in 2

2.
The best number sentence for this diagram is:
(a) 2 + 4 = 6 (b) 2 x 3 = 6
(c) 8 - 2 = 6 (d) 3 + 3 = 6

3. Complete the next 2 numbers in the pattern:

| 5 | 8 | 10 | 6 | 15 | 4 | | |

4. I bought 20 marbles and half as many stamps. The marbles were 10 for 50¢ and stamps were 10¢ each.
Total cost = $_____

5. Join the dots to form squares. The area of shape [   ] is 3 x the area of shape [   ].

6. Complete the last line by following the pattern:
47¢ x 10 = $4.70
23¢ x 10 = $2.30
68¢ x 10 = $6.80
76¢ x 10 = $_____

7. Draw the pattern in box B after box A has had a $\frac{1}{4}$ clockwise turn.

A   B [   ]

8. 6 + 6 + 6 gives the same answer as:
(a) 3 + 9 + 3 (b) (6 x 2) + (6 x 1)
(c) (6 + 6) x 3 (d) 6 x 6 x 6

9.  Show 1500 hours on the clock.
The hour hand is shorter.

10. [   ] + [   ] + [   ] + 5 = 65
The missing numbers are all different and are all multiples of 10.

11.

This hexagonal prism has [   ] edges.

12. Think about the $\frac{1}{2}$ and use your calculator to work out this sum:

72 x $\frac{1}{2}$ x 24 = [   ]

13. Draw a line to divide this shape into 2 congruent (equal) parts.
You will need a ruler.

14.

Degrees Celsius

```
40
30
20
10
 0
   S  M  T  W  T  F  S
```

The difference between the highest and lowest temperatures during this week was _____ degrees Celsius.

15. Shade the balloon which contains a number that can be divided exactly by 4, 5 and 10.

(25) (30) (20) (50)

Mental Math Workouts - Set 5

name:.....................

1. The answer to 294 x 7 is:
- (a) 1664
- (b) 2058
- (c) 2116
- (c) 1824

2. Use the patterns to complete the last line:

(3 x 5) + 1 = 10 + 6
(3 x 5) + 3 = 10 + 8
(3 x 5) + 5 = 10 + 10
(3 x 5) + 7 = 10 + 12

(☐ x ☐) + ☐ = ☐ + ☐

3. 27 x ☐ = 0

4. These are the 4 arrays for the number 6. Draw all the arrays for the number 8.

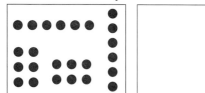

5. A _____ B _____
C _____ D _____

Line B is ☐ cm shorter than line C but

☐ cm longer than line A or line D.

6. Circle the numbers which can be divided into 2 equal whole numbers:

17 8 21 26 13 12 5

7.

2 m 32 cm = 2.32 m
5 m 3 cm = 5.03 m
so 8 m 72 cm = _____ m
7 m 5 cm = _____ m

8. How many times bigger is the underlined 3 than the other 3 in the number 2,3<u>4</u>3?
- (a) 30 times
- (b) 300 times
- (c) 10 times
- (d) 100 times

9.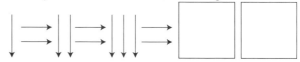

= $ _____

10. Complete the next 2 arrow diagrams:

11. Put down the 20th letter, the 15th letter and the second last letter of the alphabet to make a word:

☐ ☐ ☐

12. Use your calculator to multiply the product of 2 and 9 by two thousand one hundred and one. Turn the calculator upside down and write the word shown in the display window: _____

13. The number of small cubes in this diagram is

_____ .

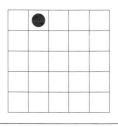

14. Move the dot 2 squares east, 3 squares south-west, one square south, and 4 squares east. Show the dot's new square.

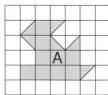

15. To find the area of shape A you would:

- (a) count only whole squares
- (b) multiply length by width
- (c) count all whole squares and half squares
- (d) count only the half squares and double them

Mental Math Workouts - Set 6

name:......................

1. Four thousand + 14 = _____

2. All square numbers can be arranged into a:
(a) rectangle   (b) cube
(c) square   (d) circle

3. Shade in the bills and coins needed to buy a $6.75 book:

$10	$5	10¢	$1	5¢	$2	20¢	50¢

4.

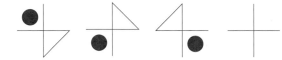

Complete the next shape in the pattern.

5.

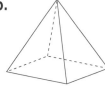 How many corners (vertices) on this pyramid with a square base?
Vertices = _____

6. Round 403 and 291 to the nearest hundred and find the sum of your 2 answers:
Sum = _____

7.

The 2nd tallest flower is_____mm high.

8. Circle the smallest number:
2,436   3,462   2,463
2,643   2,346   2,634

9.

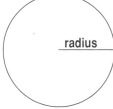
radius

A circle's radius is half its diameter. This circle's diameter is
_____ mm

10. Complete the next 3 counting numbers:

996, 997, 998, _____ , _____ , _____

11. _____ g + _____ g + 500 g = 1 kg.

12.

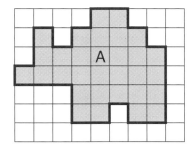
A

The perimeter of shape A on this $^1/_2$-cm grid is _____ cm.

13.

On this block graph group [ ] scored 30 points more than group [ ] and 10 more than group D.

14.

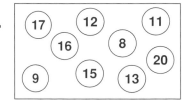

Shade the 2 circles which total (add up to) 30.

15. _____ small cubes have to be added to this shape to make a 3-cm cube.

Mental Math Workouts - Set 7

name:.....................

1.

	TT	T	H	T	U
24 x 10 =			2	4	0
24 x 100 =		2	4	0	0
24 x 1,000 =					

2.
8 x 12 = 4 x 24
6 x 10 = 3 x 20
20 x 4 = 10 x 8
16 x 5 = ☐ x ☐

Look at the doubling and halving pattern to find the missing numbers.

3. Circle the numbers which will be even numbers when they are doubled:

6    $\frac{1}{2}$ 3 $1\frac{1}{2}$

$2\frac{1}{2}$ 5 $3\frac{1}{2}$ 21

4. In one minute I could skip about:
(a) 10 times   (b) 50 times
(c) 400 times   (d) 5 times

5.

Football   4 (12) 5   Hockey

This Venn diagram shows that 17 pupils like hockey.
How many like football? _____

6. 80 cm + 40 cm + 30 cm = _____ m

7.

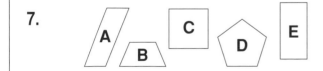

Shade the shape that is different.

8.

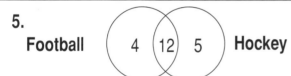

| 4 | 2 | 5 | 3 |

Shade the square number in the above shapes.

9. $1 is made up of: four 20¢ coins + one 10¢ coin + _____ 5¢ coins.

10. To find the perimeter of this shape (a closed curve) I would use:
(a) my ruler
(b) a click wheel
(c) a ruler and string
(d) a compass

11.

Use your ruler to measure and then shade the 2 shapes (polygons) with the same perimeter.

12. ☐ groups of 19 = 133
(Use a calculator!)

13.

November

S	M	T	W	T	F	S
			1	2	3	4
5	6	7	8	9	10	11
12	13	14	15	16	17	18
19	20	21	22	23	24	25
26	27	28	29	30		

Using the number patterns circle the date which is 14 days after 8 November.

14. ○○○○○○○○○○

Shade the fourth circle to the right of the center circle above.

15. Complete the last shape of the rotating pattern below:

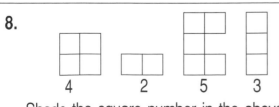

Mental Math Workouts - Set 8

name:......................

1. VIII + IX + IV = ☐

2. Join some dots to make a right-angled triangle.

3. The answer to the sum 3 x 1 x 3 x 5 is
| ODD | EVEN | (shade your answer).

4. Complete the next 2 numbers in the series:
AB12, **CD10**, **EF8**, **GH6**, _____ , _____

5.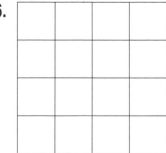
Circle the sphere and the cylinder.

6.
On this 1-cm grid draw a shape with a perimeter of 8 cm. Do not draw a square.

7. The fraction shaded is:
(a) $\frac{1}{2}$ (b) $\frac{2}{3}$
(c) $\frac{3}{4}$ (d) $\frac{2}{6}$

8. Circle the odd numbers:
7   12   24   37   276   359   1,021

9.
_____ and _____ are taller than _____ who is taller than _____ who is the shortest.

10. Eight hundreds – 500 = _____ .

11. All even numbers can be divided exactly by:
(a) 10   (b) 6
(c) 2   (d) 4

12. 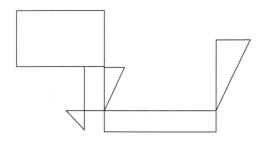 Three and 4 will divide into 24 exactly so it is shaded. Shade other numbers which have the same 2 factors.

13. This shape has one outside region and _____ inside regions.

14. A —— B —— C
D —— E —— F —
I could use lines ☐B☐ and ☐F☐ and ☐ and ☐ to make a rectangle.

15. Ann planned to save 50¢ a week for 8 weeks. In the 5th week she saved twice her usual amount. How much did she save in the 8 weeks?

Savings = $ _____

Mental Math Workouts - Set 9

name:.....................

1. Complete the pattern of square numbers below:

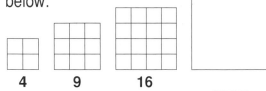

4   **9**   **16**   _____

2. If you rearrange the digits of 185 you can make the numbers:

158, 851, 815, 518 and [____].

3.   Draw hands on the clock to show 11:10 a.m. The hour hand is shorter.

4. 7 rods + 3 ones + 2 flats =

H   T   U

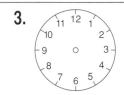

5. The difference between 10 and 17 is the same as the difference between:

(a) 17 and 11   (b) 15 and 21
(c) 9 and 16   (d) 8 and 18

6.

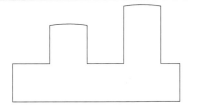

I estimate the perimeter of this shape is about:
(a) 30 cm   (b) 8 cm
(c) 16 cm   (d) 22 cm

7.

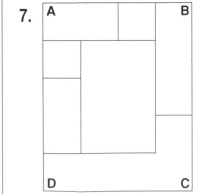

Complete the lines in shape ABCD to divide it into squares.

Its area =

_____ squares

(cm²)

8.   A _____

Half of line A is _____ cm or _____ mm.
Use a ruler.

9. In a class of 28, ten children were at sports practice and half of the rest at choir practice. How many children were left in the classroom? _____ children.

10. If you double the length of each side of shape A, the new shape has _____ times as many squares in its area.

11.
(5   x   12)   -   10   =   50
(4   x   12)   -   8   =   40   Use the
(3   x   12)   -   6   =   30   number
(2   x   12)   -   4   =   20   patterns.

([ ] x [ ]) - [ ] = [ ]

12.   [ ] + [ ] + [ ] = 1

13. The numbers in the boxes are all multiples of 4. Write the missing multiple of 4 which is less than 40.

8	36	12
16		4
24	28	20

14.

BOOKS READ: MAY, TIM, AMY, ROB, ROY

0 10 20 30 40 50 60

This bar graph shows that _____ has read four times the books as _____ .

15. The total length of all edges in this prism = _____ cm.

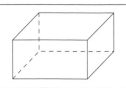

Mental Math Workouts - Set 10

name:.......................

1. 2 x 10 | **>** | **<** | **=** | 4 x 8
Shade the box which makes a true math sentence.

2. 200 g x ☐ = 1 kg

3.
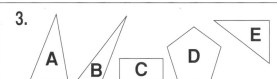
Shade the shape which has only one right angle.

4. An odd number + another odd number always gives an | **ODD** | **EVEN** | number. Shade your answer.

5. I estimate my teacher's height to be
_____ cm.

6. Circle the objects which are longer than one meter:

pencil	broom	tray
bed	bat	book

7.
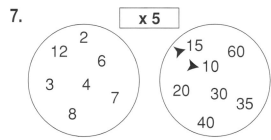
Draw the rest of the arrows to complete this mapping diagram by using the relation sign in the box.

8. A rectangle's length is twice its width. Its perimeter is 24 cm. Its measurements are:
(a) 4 and 2 cm   (b) 6 and 3 cm
(c) 10 and 5 cm   (d) 8 and 4 cm

9. Circle the fraction which is less than $^1/_2$:
$^7/_8$ $^3/_4$ $^5/_{10}$ $^3/_8$ $^6/_{12}$

10. Use the number patterns to complete:

(12	x	5)	–	0	=	60
(12	x	6)	–	2	=	70
(12	x	7)	–	4	=	80
(12	x	8)	–	6	=	90

(☐ x ☐) - ☐ = ☐

11.
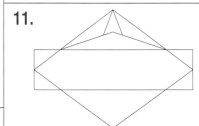
Color the right-angled triangles in this diagram.

12.

DAVID   JUNE   AMY   PETER

_____ is the shortest as he is shorter than _____ and _____ , who are both taller than _____ .

13. Complete this money math sentence:
$5 + $2 + 20¢ =
$2 + $2 + $2 + 10¢ + 10¢ + _____

14.

	4 x Table	5 x Table	
		5	Odd
12			Even

Use the numbers **less than 20** that fit into the Carroll diagram. Two have been done for you.

15. The longest side of this 6-sided shape is
_____ cm or
_____ mm longer than its shortest side.

Mental Math Workouts - Set 11

1. Any even number divided by itself gives an answer which is:
(a) odd or even   **(b)** even
(c) not odd or even   **(d)** odd

2.
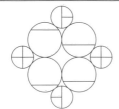
Color in one semi-circle in this diagram.

3. $\neq$ **>** **<** **=** $\div$
Use one of these symbols to make this math sentence true: $^5/_{10}$ ☐ $^4/_8$

4. Circle the digital clock which shows 4 p.m..

4:30 | 14:00
16:00 | 18:00

5. Put these fractions in order from smallest to largest: $^1/_2$ $^1/_4$ $^1/_{10}$ _____

6. If two odd numbers are added to any even number, the answer is always:
(a) correct   (b) even
(c) odd   (d) odd or even

7. A tennis ball weighs about:
(a) 2 g   (b) 50 g
(c) 2 kg   (d) 5 kg

8.
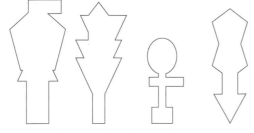
Circle the shape which is balanced on either side of a line drawn down its center.

9.
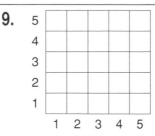
Shade grid square (2, 5) and put a X in grid square (4, 3).

10.
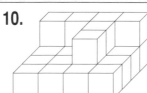
How many small cubes would I have if I doubled the number in this shape? _____

11. Share $22 among John, Mary and Rhonda so Mary gets 3 times as much as John and twice as much as Rhonda.
Mary's share   = $ _____
John's share   = $ _____
Rhonda's share   = $ _____

12. Draw 2 lines to divide this shape into 3 congruent (equal) rectangles.

13.   is half of
2½ 3½ 13 0.5 7 17
7 26 34 5 1 ►14
Draw the rest of the arrows to complete this mapping diagram.

14. Shade the number which is the product of 2 other numbers in the circle.
24 5 18 7 32 36
37 31 4 40 6 21

15. Using only the numbers up to twenty fill in the Venn diagram.
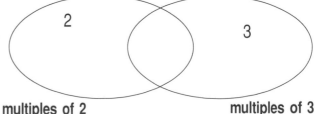
2   3
multiples of 2   multiples of 3

name:.......................

1. 2 x 12 = ☐ + ☐ + ☐
The missing numbers are all the same.

2. Follow the pattern to find the missing numbers:

| **3,000** | + | **300** | + | ☐ | + | ☐ | = 3,333 |

3. To walk around a basketball court would take me about:
(a) 10 mins   (b) 20 mins
(c) 1 min   (d) 5 mins

4. 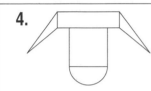 There are _____ different kinds of shapes in this diagram.

5. Color the shapes which will **tessellate** (fit together without gaps between the shapes).

6. Rounding 358 to the nearest ten is:
(a)   350   (b)   300
(c)   360   (d)   355

7.
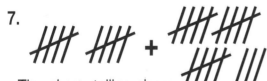
The above tallies show:
(a) 8 + 15   (b) 10 + 15
(b) 4 + 6   (d) 10 + 18

8. I have $24. Tim has twice as much and Ann has $8 less than my amount. How much do we have altogether? $_____

9. There are no [ODD] [EVEN] multiples of 4 because 4 is an [ODD] [EVEN] number. Shade your answers.

10. 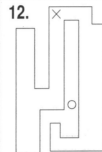 If I draw all the diagonals in this pentagon (5-sided shape) the number of small triangles formed would be:
(a) 8   (b) 12 (c) 9   (d) 10

11. 50 + 100 + 50 + 50 + 100 + 50 + 200 + 50 + 200
How many fifties do we have if we add the above numbers? _____

12. The X is in the [INSIDE] [OUTSIDE] region of this shape and the dot is in the [INSIDE] [OUTSIDE] region. Shade your answers.

13.

August

S	M	T	W	T	F	S
	1	2	3	4	5	6
7	8	9	10	11	12	13
14	15	16	17	18	19	20
21	22	23	24	25	26	27
28	29	30	31			

The total number of Tuesdays and Fridays in this month is

_____ .

14. The total length of the **vertical** lines in this shape is

_____ cm or

_____ mm.

15.

Math   Spelling

There are 24 children in a class. Thirteen like math and spelling. Five like spelling only and 6 like math only. Show this information on the diagram.

Mental Math Workouts - *Set 1 Review*

name:.....................

1. Six tens + 45 = _____

2. To the nearest centimeter which line below is 5 cm long? _____

A _____
B _____
C _____
D _____

3. Write the smallest number you can make with the figures **4 1 7 3**:

_____

4. Shade the fraction $^1/_8$ in one of these diagrams:

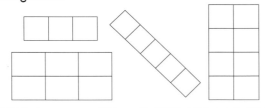

5. Complete the last basic number fact in the set below:

7 x 5 = 35   35 ÷ 5 = 7

5 x 7 = 35   ⬚ ÷ ⬚ = ⬚

6. Write the number seven thousand and two.

_____

7.

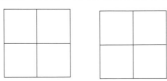

How many smaller cubes would you stack on these grids to make 2 larger cubes? _____

8. Think about the $^1/_2$ and use your calculator to work out this sum:

($^1/_2$ of 158) + 21 = _____

9. Color the latest time shown on the clocks.

10:15 14:25
13:00 19:30

10.

Complete the last 2 shapes in the pattern.

11. The shaded part of this shape is:

(a) $^1/_5$
(b) $^1/_4$
(c) a fraction of the whole
(d) $^1/_{10}$

12. An ant walked _____ cm from A to B on this network of paths.

13. Use the number patterns to complete the last line:

5   x   4   =   18   +   2
5   x   5   =   21   +   4
5   x   6   =   24   +   6
5   x   7   =   27   +   8
⬚   x   ⬚   =   ⬚   +   ⬚

14.

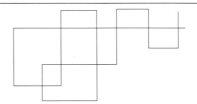

There are _____ inside regions in this shape.

15. Fill in the missing numbers in this clockwise pattern.

3	2	6	2		2	
■						2
						15
33						
2						2
	2	27	2			21

Mental Math Workouts - Set 2 Review

name:.....................

1. ☐ ÷ 3 = 8

2. I estimate the height of the teacher's desk is _____ cm.

3. 73 rounded to the nearest ten is _____ .

4. Pens are 24¢ each. If I buy a pack of three for 60¢ I save myself _____ cents.

5. 6 × ☐ = 4 × 12

6. When zero is multiplied by any number the answer is:
   (a) always one
   (b) more than one
   (c) zero
   (d) same as the number

7. This shape is divided into:
   (a) thirds
   (b) triangles
   (c) three parts
   (d) fourths

8. XIX – XV = _____

9.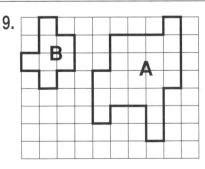
   The area of shape A is:
   (a) 2   (b) 3
   (c) 4   (d) 5
   × shape B's area.

10. This diagram shows that the fraction $\frac{1}{2}$ is the same as the fraction _____ .

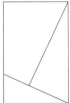

HALVES

TENTHS

11.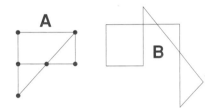

Group _____ has 3 times as many points as group _____ but only half of group _____'s points on this block graph.

12.

There are 6 intersections in diagram A and _____ intersections in diagram B.

13. These are 2 of the arrays for the number 4. Draw the 3 arrays for 9 in the box.

14. This prism has _____ vertices (corners).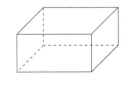

15. The diameter of a circle is twice its radius.
The radius of this circle is _____ mm.

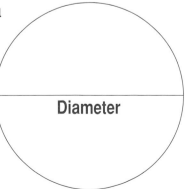

Diameter

Mental Math Workouts - Set 3 Review

name:.....................

1. Shade the odd multiples of 5.

5	8	10	12	15	20	25	28

2. If you double an odd number the answer is:
   (a) always odd
   (b) odd or even
   (c) not odd or even
   (d) always even

3. Put a X in grid square (E,4) and shade grid square (B,2).

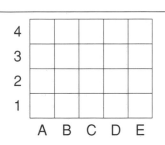

4.
   80   x   10   =   800
   40   x   20   =   800
   20   x   40   =   800

   ☐   x   ☐   =   ☐

5.

Dad is

_____ cm

tall.

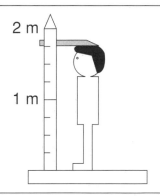

6. Complete the next domino in this pattern.

7. This is a closed curve with one intersection. Draw a closed curve with 3 intersections in the box.

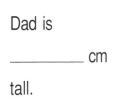

8. ● ○ ● ● ○ ● ● ● ○

_____ out of _____ circles are shaded which means $^7/_{10}$ are shaded.

9. A _____
B
Draw a line B that is 3 times longer than A and divide the new line into 2 equal lengths.

10. I throw two dice and a 5 and a 3 come up. My next throw will be:
   (a) a 5 and 3   (b) two 5's
   (c) two 3's   (d) I can't tell.

11. Four fifties + 34 =

H	T	U

12.

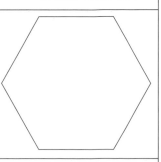

△ x ☐ x △ = 20

The missing numbers are all prime numbers.

13. Use the addition pattern to complete the missing numbers.

16	2	12
6		
8		4

14. Draw a vertical line and a horizontal line inside this hexagon to form 2 right-angled triangles and 2 quadrilaterals.

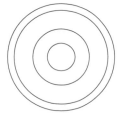

15. Concentric circles have the same center. The width of the third largest concentric circle shown is

_____ mm.

Mental Math Workouts - Set 4 Review

name:.......................

1. An odd number x an odd number:
  (a) is always even
  (b) is odd or even
  (c) always ends in 3
  (d) is always odd

2.
  The best number sentence for this diagram is:
  (a) 12 – 3 = 9   (b) 5 + 4 = 9
  (c) 3 x 3 = 9   (d) 8 + 1 = 9

3. Complete the next 2 numbers in the pattern:

  | 3 | 25 | 6 | 20 | 9 | 15 | | |

4. When Peter gave me half his marbles he had 18 left. How many did he have originally?

  _____ marbles.

5.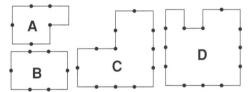

  Join the dots to form squares. The area of

  shape ____ is 3 x the area of shape ____ .

6. Complete the last line.
  43¢   x   100   = $ 43.00
  37¢   x   100   = $ 37.00
  26¢   x   100   = $ 26.00
  58¢   x   100   = $ _____

7. Draw the pattern in box B after box A has had a $^1/_4$ turn clockwise.
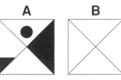

8. 4 + 4 + 4 gives the same answer as:
  (a) (4 + 4) x 4   (b) 4 x 4 x 4
  (c) (4 x 2) + (4 x 1)   (d) (4 x 1) + 4

9. Show 1400 hours on the clock. The hour hand is shorter.

10.
  The missing numbers are all different even numbers.

11. Think about the $^1/_2$ and use your calculator to work out this sum:

  48 x $^1/_2$ x 25 = _____

12. This pentagonal prism has

  _____ edges.
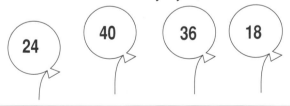

13. Draw 2 lines to divide this shape into 4 congruent (equal) squares. You will need to measure with your ruler.

14. Shade the balloon which contains a number that can be divided exactly by 3, 4 and 9.

15. This line graph of Amy's test results shows that her highest mark was _____ and her lowest was

  _____ .

Mental Math Workouts - *Set 5 Review*

name:......................

1. The answer to 326 x 3 is:
   (a) 946   (b) 924
   (c) 978   (d) 942

2. Use the patterns to complete the last line:

$$(5 \times 5) + 2 = 20 + 7$$
$$(5 \times 5) + 4 = 21 + 8$$
$$(5 \times 5) + 6 = 22 + 9$$
$$(5 \times 5) + 8 = 23 + 10$$

(⬚ x ⬚) + ⬚ = ⬚ + ⬚

3. 6 x ⬚ x ⬚ = 0

4. Draw the 4 possible arrays for the number 10 in the box.

5. A _____
   B _____
   C _____
   D _____

Line ⬚ is 2 cm longer than line ⬚ but

1 cm less than line ⬚ .

6. Circle the numbers which can be divided into 3 equal numbers:

   16 15 20 21 23 42 99

7.
   5 m 68 cm = 5.68 m
   3 m   8 cm = 3.08 m
   7 m 15 cm = 7.15 m
so 6 m 23 cm = _____ m
   2 m   7 cm = _____ m

8. How many times bigger is the underlined 5 than the other 5 in the number 3,5̲56?
   (a) 5 times   (b) 50 times
   (c) 10 times   (d) 100 times

9. Complete the next arrow diagram:

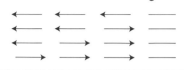

10. Write the 4th letter after D, the 15th letter and the 7th letter from the end of the alphabet to form the word:

⬚ ⬚ ⬚

11. $5 + 50¢ + $1

= $2 + $2 + 50¢ + $1 + _____

12. VII x 1,000 + 100 + V = ?
Use your calculator to do this sum. Then turn the calculator upside down and write the word shown in the display window.

⬚ ⬚ ⬚ ⬚

13. Move the dot 2 squares south east, then
3 squares north,
2 squares east,
4 squares south west.
Show the dot's new square.

14. The number of small cubes in this diagram = _____ .

15. The area of shape A equals _____ squares. (don't forget to count $^1/_2$ squares too!).

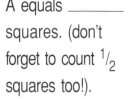

name:.......................

1. Five thousand + 12 = _____ .

2. Square numbers are:
   (a) always odd   (b) odd or even
   (c) always even   (d) not odd or even

3. Shade the notes and coins needed to buy
   a toy for $11.35.

$10	5¢	20¢	$5	50¢	$2	10¢	$1

4. Complete the next square in this pattern:

5. The base of this
   pyramid is a triangle, so
   it has _____
   vertices (corners).

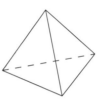

6. Circle the smallest number:

   2,138   2,813   2,381

   2,318   2,831   2,183

7. Round 326 and 184 to the nearest
   hundred and find the sum of your 2
   answers: _____

8.

The third tallest flower is _____ mm high.

9. Complete the next 3 counting numbers:

   1,098   1,099   _____

   _____   _____

10. A circle's radius
   is half its
   diameter.
   This circle's
   diameter is

   _____ mm
   (use a ruler).

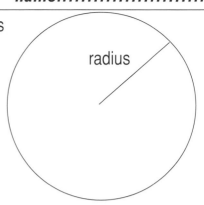
radius

11. $\frac{1}{2}$ kg + _____ g + _____ g = 1kg

12.

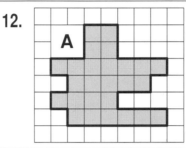
A

The perimeter
of shape A on
this $\frac{1}{2}$ -cm grid
is _____ cm.

13.

On this block graph group **A** collected

twice as many cans as group _____ , but

only half as many as group _____ .

14. Shade the 2 circles
   which total (add up to) XXV.

   (IX) (XXI) (XII) (XVI) (VII) (XIV) (XV)

15. _____ small
   cubes have to be
   added to this shape
   to make a
   3 cm cube
   (i.e. a cube with
   all sides 3 cm long).

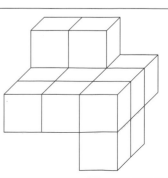

Mental Math Workouts - Set 7 Review

name:......................

1.

	TT	T	H	T	U
37 x 10 =			3	7	0
37 x 100 =		3	7	0	0
37 x 1,000 =					

2.
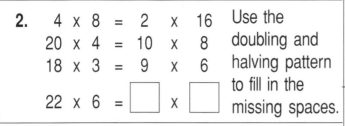
4 x 8 = 2 x 16
20 x 4 = 10 x 8
18 x 3 = 9 x 6
22 x 6 = ☐ x ☐

Use the doubling and halving pattern to fill in the missing spaces.

3. Circle the numbers which will be odd numbers when they are doubled:

4   7 $2^1/_2$ 6

5          $1^1/_2$ 3 $3^1/_2$

4. My pencil would weigh about:
(a) 2 kg   **(b)** 10 g
(c) 10 kg   **(d)** 100 g

5.
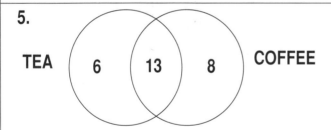
TEA   6   13   8   COFFEE

This Venn diagram shows that 21 adults like coffee. How many like tea? _____

6. 1 m 20 cm + 70 cm + 60 cm = _____ m

7. Shade the shape which is different from the others.

8.
 6   4
2   5

Shade the triangular number in the above shapes.

9. $3 is made up of:
five 20¢ coins + two 50¢ coins + six 10¢ coins + _____ 5¢ coins.

10. To find the perimeter of shape A I would use:
(a) a ruler and string
(b) a compass
(c) a guess
(d) a click wheel
(e) a ruler

11. Complete the last shape of the pattern.

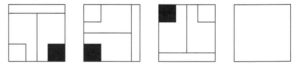

12. Use your ruler to measure and then shade the 2 polygons with the same perimeter.

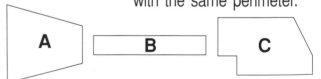

A   B   C

13. What is the total number of Mondays and Fridays in this month? _____

		August				
S	M	T	W	T	F	S
	1	2	3	4	5	6
7	8	9	10	11	12	13
14	15	16	17	18	19	20
21	22	23	24	25	26	27
28	29	30	31			

14. Use your calculator to find how many groups of 24 there are in 6,000. _____ groups.

15. Shade 3 semi-circles, one to the left of the center circle and two to the right.

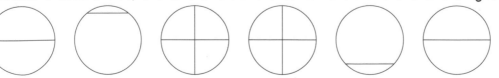

Mental Math Workouts - Set 8 Review

1. XIX + IV + VII = ☐ Answer in Roman numerals.

2. Join some dots to make 2 right-angled triangles.

3. The answer to the sum 2 x 6 x 4 x 2 is ☐ ODD ☐ EVEN (shade your answer).

4. Complete the next 2 numbers in the series:

AA4 AB6 AC8 AD10 _____ _____

5. Circle the 2 solid shapes with the same number of faces:

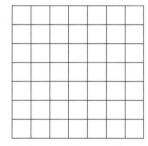

6.

On this $\frac{1}{2}$-cm grid draw a shape which has a perimeter of 7 cm.

7. Circle the even numbers:

8   1,033   2,768   2,911   3,020   77   1,084

8. The fraction shaded is:

(a) $\frac{3}{4}$
(b) $\frac{1}{2}$
(c) $\frac{5}{8}$
(d) $\frac{4}{4}$

9.

_____ and _____ are both taller

than _____ but shorter than _____ .

10. Eight hundreds − four fifties

= two fifties + _____ .

11. If an even number can be exactly divided by 4 it can also be exactly divided by:

(a) 8   (b) 3   (c) 2   (d) 12

12. The numbers 2, 3 and 4 will all divide into 24 exactly so it is shaded. Shade other numbers which have the same 3 factors.

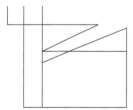

24	28	20
30	36	16
40	12	60

13. This shape has one outside region and _____ inside regions.

14. A _____
      B _____
    C _____
      D _____
    E _____
  F _____

I could use lines ☐ , ☐ , ☐ and ☐ to make a rectangle (use a ruler).

15. Share $20 among three girls so that Amy has four times as much as Ann who has $2 less than Toni.

Amy $ _____

Ann $ _____

Toni $ _____

Mental Math Workouts - Set 9 Review

name:......................

1.

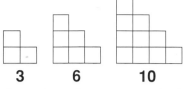

3   6   10   ___

Complete the pattern of triangular numbers.

2. If you rearrange the digits of 274 you can make the numbers:

247, 724, 472, 427 and [   ] .

Circle the smallest number.

3.

Draw the hands on the clock to show 10:40 p.m..

4.

            H T U

5 rods + 7 ones + 4 flats = [| |] .

5. The product of 6 and 4 is the same as the product of:

(a) 7 and 5   (b) 3 and 9
(c) 3 and 8   (d) 5 and 6

6.

I estimate the length of this line to be about:

(a) 15 cm   (b) 9 cm
(c) 25 cm   (d) 6 cm

7.

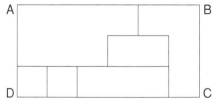

Complete the lines in the shape ABCD above to divide it into squares.

Its area is _____ squares.

8.   A _____

Half of line A above is _____ cm or

_____ mm (use a ruler).

9. John and Sue shared 24 marbles so that Sue had twice as many as John.

John had _____ marbles.

Sue had _____ marbles.

10. (6 x 4) = 20 + 4   Use the number
(6 x 5) = 24 + 6   patterns to
(6 x 6) = 28 + 8   complete the last
(6 x 7) = 32 + 10   line.

([ ] x [ ]) = [ ] + [ ]

11. [ ] + [ ] = [ ] + [ ]

The missing numbers are the first 4 counting numbers.

12.

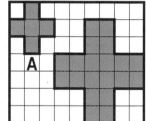

If you double the length of each side of shape A the new shape has _____ times as many squares in its area.

13.

3	15	24
27		9
12	18	6

The numbers in the boxes are all multiples of 3. Write in the missing multiple of 3 which is less than 30.

14. The total length of all edges on this prism

= _____ cm

(use a ruler).

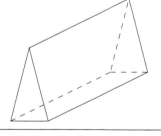

15.

       0 10 20 30 40 50 60 70 80

This bar graph shows that [   ] has seen 3 times as many films as [   ] .

Mental Math Workouts - Set 10 Review

name:.....................

1. 20 x 3 [>] [<] [=] 5 x 11

2. 100 mL x [   ] = 1 L

3. Shade the shape which has no right angles.

A   B   C   D   E

4. An odd number + two even numbers always give an [ODD EVEN] number. Shade your answer.

5. I estimate the height of my desk to be _____ cm.

6. Circle the objects which are heavier than one kilogram:

pencil   C.D.   door
brick   balloon   car

7. Circle the fraction which is more than one half:
$\frac{4}{10}$ $\frac{1}{5}$ $\frac{5}{8}$ $\frac{1}{3}$ $\frac{2}{4}$

8. A rectangle's length is 10 cm. Its perimeter is 28 cm. Its measurements are:

(a) 10 cm and 6 cm   (b) 10 cm and 5 cm
(c) 8 cm and 10 cm   (d) 10 cm and 4 cm

9.   [x 4]

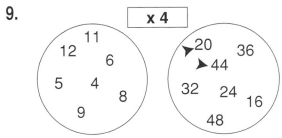

Draw the rest of the arrows to complete this diagram by using the relation sign in the box.

10. [$5] + (50¢) + (20¢) =
($2) + ($1) + (50¢) + [   ] + (20¢)

11. Use the number patterns to complete the last line:

(2	x	4)	=	10	–	2
(4	x	4)	=	20	–	4
(6	x	4)	=	30	–	6
(8	x	4)	=	40	–	8
([ ]	x	[ ])	=	[ ]	–	[ ]

12. Color the 4-sided shapes (quadrilaterals) in this diagram.

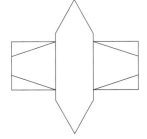

13.

	5 x Table	11 x Table	
		11	Odd
	10		Even

Use the numbers **less than 35** to fit into the Carroll diagram. Two have been done for you.

14.

The longest side of this 8-sided shape (octagon) is _____ cm or _____ mm longer than its shortest side.

15.

ALAN   PAT   JEAN   MARY

[   ] is taller than [   ] and
[   ] but shorter than [   ].

Mental Math Workouts - Set 11 Review

name:........................

1. Any odd number divided by itself gives an answer which is:
   (a) odd or even **(b)** even
   (c) odd **(d)** not odd or even

2. 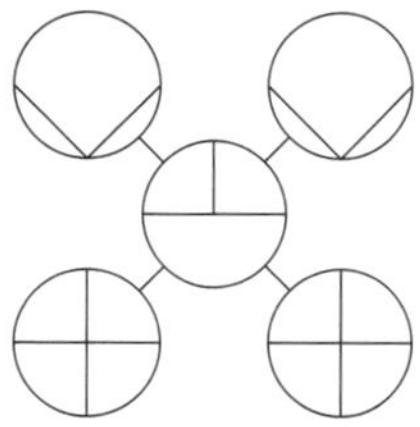
   Color the one semi-circle in the diagram.

3. > = < ÷ X
   Use one of these symbols to make this math sentence true:

   15 + 20 ☐ 5 x 7

4. 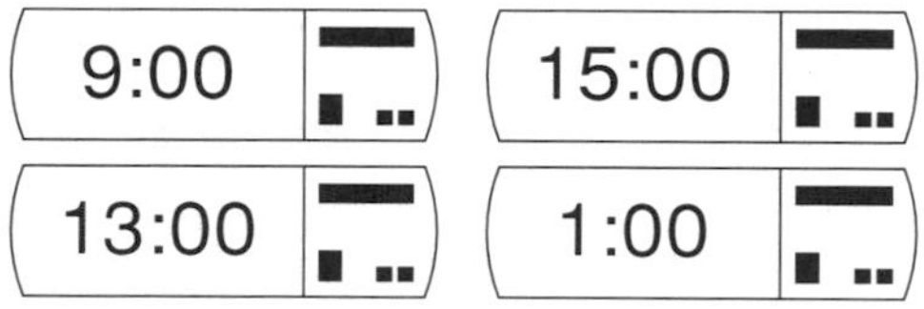
9:00
15:00
13:00
1:00
   Circle the digital clock which shows 1 p.m..

5. Put these fractions in order from lowest to highest: $^1/_4$ $^1/_{20}$ $^1/_2$

   ⁄ , ⁄ , ⁄

6. If 2 even numbers are added to any odd number the answer is always:
   (a) even (b) odd or even
   (c) correct (d) odd

7. 4 cm^2 is about the area of:
   (a) a door (b) a book
   (c) a stamp (d) a pool

8. Circle the shape which is balanced on either side of a line drawn across its center from left to right.
   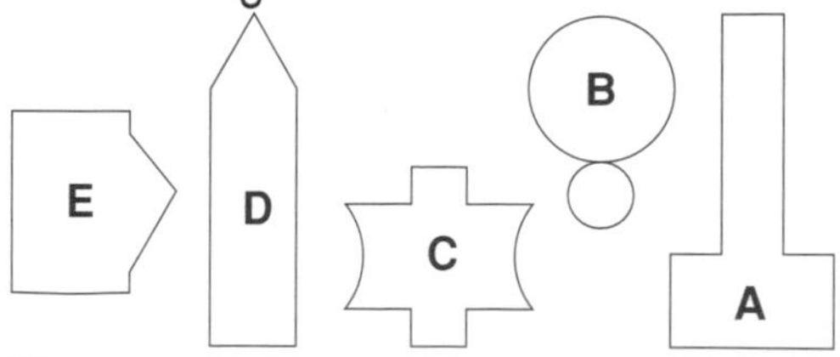
E
D
C
B
A

9. 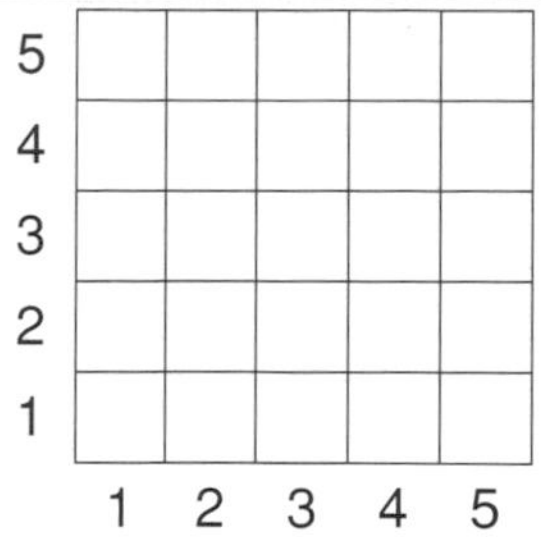
5
4
3
2
1
1 2 3 4 5
   Shade in grid square (5, 3) and put a X in grid square (2, 4).

10. 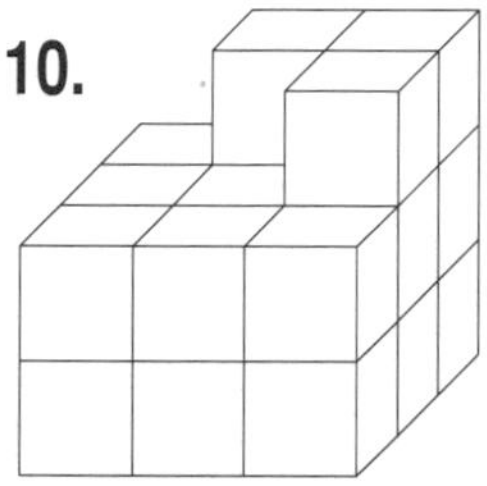
   How many small cubes would I have if I doubled the number in this shape?
   ________ small cubes.

11. Share $30 among Roy, Ann and Peta so Ann gets three times as much as Roy and $5 more than Peta.
   Ann's share $ ________
   Peta's share $ ________
   Roy's share $ ________

12. Draw 3 lines to divide this shape into 4 congruent (equal) triangles.
   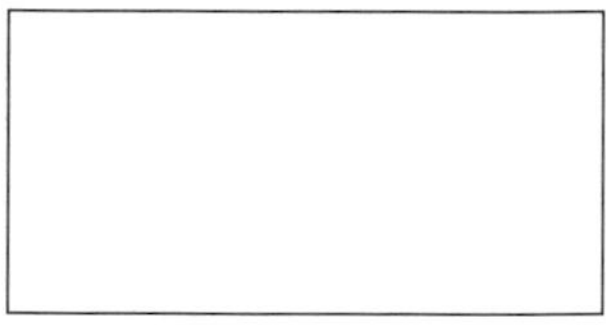

13. 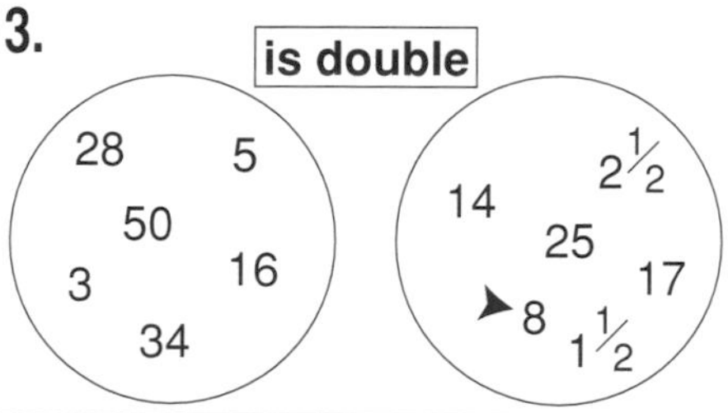
is double
28
5
50
3
16
34
14
$2\frac{1}{2}$
25
17
8
$1\frac{1}{2}$
   Complete this mapping diagram.

14. 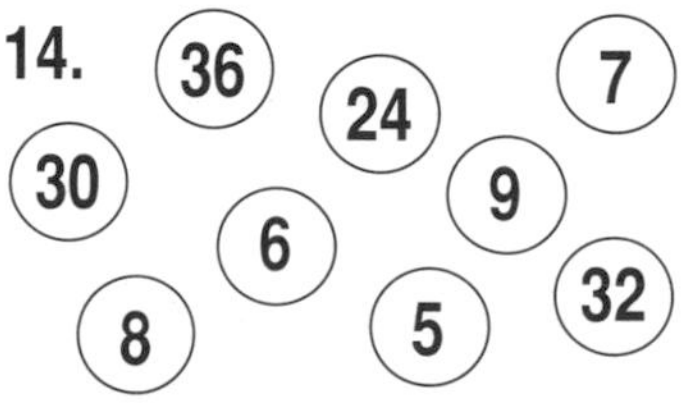
36
24
7
30
9
6
32
8
5
   Shade the number which is the product of 2 other numbers in the circle.

15. Fill in this Venn diagram with numbers **up to 25.**
   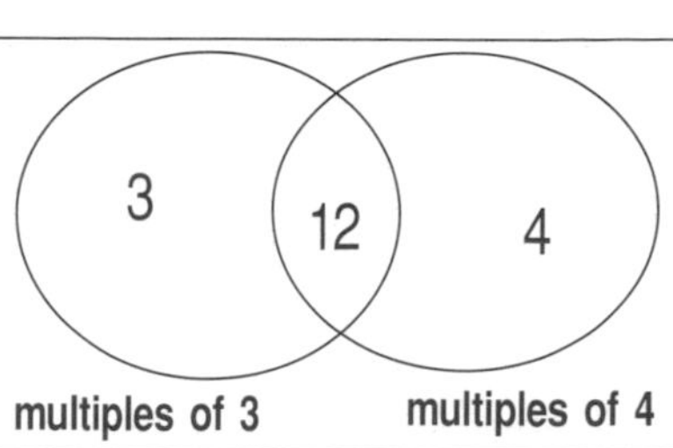
3
12
4
multiples of 3
multiples of 4

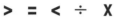

name:.......................

1. 4 + 4 + 4 = ☐ + (2 x ☐)

The missing numbers are both the same.

2. 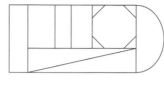 There are _____ different kinds of shapes in this diagram.

3. If I counted from 1 to 10 with a second between each number it would take me:

(a) 10 seconds   **(b)** 8 seconds
(c) 9 seconds   **(d)** 11 seconds

4. Follow the pattern to find the missing numbers:

☐ + ☐ + ☐ + ☐ = 5,555

5. Shade the shapes which will **tessellate** (i.e. fit together without gaps between the shapes).

6. Rounding 2,537 to the nearest ten is:

(a) 2,530   **(b)** 2,540
(c) 2,400   **(d)** 2,545

7.

The above tallies show:

(a) 4 + 3   (b) 10 + 10
(c) 13 + 12   (d) 13 + 13

8. I have $10. Roy has twice as much and Jane has half as much. How much do we have altogether? $ _____

9. 50 + 200 + 200 + 50 + 100 + 100
How many fifties do we have if we add the above numbers?

_____ fifties.

10. The total length of the **horizontal** lines in this shape is _____ cm or _____ mm.

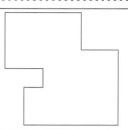

11. If I rule all the diagonals in this hexagon (6-sided shape) the number of triangles formed would be:

(a) 6   **(b)** 20
(c) 18   **(d)** 24

12. The **X** is in the

| INSIDE | OUTSIDE |

region of the shape and the dot is in the

| INSIDE | OUTSIDE |

region.
Shade your answers.

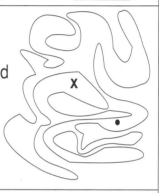

13.

| December | | | | | | |
S	M	T	W	T	F	S
			1	2	3	4	5
6	7	8	9	10	11	12
13	14	15	16	17	18	19
20	21	22	23	24	25	26
27	28	29	30	31		

The total number of Mondays and Thursdays in this month is _____ .

14. There are no | ODD | EVEN | multiples of ten because 10 is an | ODD | EVEN | number.
Shade your answers.

15. There are 31 children in a class. 14 like art and sport. 8 like only sport. How many like only art? Use the Venn diagram below to find out.

SPORT   ART

8   14

Mental Math Workouts (Answers 1)

Set 1

1. 63
2. 5,321
3. (b)
4. ■□□□□
5. 36 ÷ 9 = 4
6. 5,012
7. 8
8. 50
9. 07:00
10. ▼ □ ▲ ▲
11. (c)
12. 7 cm
13. 3 x 8 = 18 + 6
14. 3 regions
15. (circle diagram: 6, 12, 18, 24, 30, 36, 42, 48)

Set 2

1. 20
2. answer varies
3. 40
4. 15¢
5. 6
6. (d)
7. (c)
8. VI
9. (c)
10. 11
11. 3, Roy
12. ⋮ , •••• , or ∷
13. 15 mm
14. 6 faces, 12 edges
15. $^2/_4$

Set 3

1. 3 4 5 6 7 8 9 10 11 12
2. (c)
3. (grid with D C B A rows, X marked)
4. 5 x 80 = 400
5. 125 cm
6. (half circle, black/white squares)
7. 3 out of 8
8. answer varies
9. 40 mm line, 10 mm segments
10. (c)
11. 427
12. 2 x 6 x 2
13. (grid: 8 1 6 / 3 5 7 / 4 9 2)
14. (trapezoid)
15. 25 mm

Set 4

1. (c)
2. (b)
3. 20, 2
4. $2.00
5. D, A
6. $7.60
7. (square with triangle/dot)
8. (b)
9. (clock)
10. 20 + 10 + 30
11. 18 edges
12. 864
13. (shape)
14. 15°C
15. 20

Set 5

1. (b)
2. 3 x 5 + 9 = 10 + 14
3. 0
4. (dot pattern)
5. 2 cm, 1 cm
6. 8, 26, 12
7. 8.72 m, 7.05 m
8. (d)
9. $8.05
10. |||| ⇒
11. toy
12. Bible
13. 14
14. (grid with dot)
15. (c)

Set 6

1. 4,014
2. (c)
3. $10 $5 10¢ $1 5¢ $2 20¢ 50¢
4. (flag shape with dot)
5. 5
6. 700
7. 25 mm
8. 2,346
9. 30 mm
10. 999 1,000 1,001
11. answer varies
12. 16 cm
13. E, B
14. 17, 13
15. 16

Set 7

1. 24,000
2. 16 x 5 = 8 x 10
3. 6, 3, 5, 21
4. (b)
5. 16
6. 1$^1/_2$ meters
7. (d) 5-sided
8. 4
9. two
10. (c)
11. rectangles have same perimeter
12. 7 lots
13. the 22nd
14. ○○○○○○○●
15. (square shape)

Set 8

1. XXI or 21
2. answers vary
3. odd
4. IJ4, KL2
5. C, D
6. answers vary
7. (a)
8. 7, 37, 359, 1021
9. Tim, May, Amy, Rod
10. 300
11. (c)
12. (grid: 24 40 48 / 18 32 12 / 36 16 28)
13. 6 inside regions
14. C, D
15. $4.50

Set 9

1. (grid), 25
2. 581
3. (clock)
4. 273
5. (c)
6. (c)
7. 20 cm^2
8. 11/2 cm, 15 mm
9. 9 children
10. 4 times
11. (1 x 12) - 2 = 10
12. answers vary
13. 32
14. Tim, Roy
15. 16 cm

Set 10

1. < (less than)
2. 5
3. E
4. even
5. answers vary
6. broom, bed
7. (circles diagram, x 5: 15→60, 20→30 35, →40)
8. (d)
9. $^3/_8$
10. 12 x 9 - 8 = 100
11. (diamond shape)
12. Peter, David, Amy, June
13. $1
14. (table: 4x Table, 5x Table, 5 15 Odd, 12 8 10 Even, 4 16)
15. 1 cm, 10 mm

Set 11

1. (d)
2. (circles diagram) either top or bottom
3. =
4. 16.00
5. $^1/_{10}$, $^1/_4$, $^1/_2$
6. (b)
7. (b)
8. (arrow shape)
9. (grid 5 4 3 2, X marked / 1 2 3 4 5)
10. 44 cubes
11. Mary $12, John $4, Rhonda, $6
12. 20 mm segments
13. (circles diagram, is half of: 2½, 3½ 13, 0.5, 17 / 7→26, 34 5, 14→1)
14. 24
15. multiples of 2 / multiples of 3 (Venn diagram: 2, 8, 20, 10, 14, 4, 16 / 6, 18, 12 / 15, 9, 3)

Set 12

1. 8 + 8 + 8   2. 3,000+300+30+3   3. (c)

4. 4   5.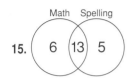

6. (c)   7. (d)   8. $88

9. odd, even   10. (d)   11. 17 fifties

12. inside, outside   13. 9   14. 13 cm, 130 mm

15. Math   Spelling

6 (13) 5

Set 1 – Review

1. 105   2. C   3. 1,347

4. [grid]   5. 35 ÷ 7 = 5   6. 7,002

7. 16   8. 100   9. 19:30

10. [grid] [diamond]   11. (c)   12. 8 cm

13. 5 x 8 = 30 + 10   14. 8   15. [grid]

Set 2 – Review

1. 24   2. answers vary   3. 70

4. 12¢   5. 8   6. (c)

7. (c)   8. IV   9. (b)

10. $5/10$ 11. B, F, C   12. 10

13. , ... , :::   14. 8 vertices

15. 25 mm

Set 3 – Review

1. | 5 | 8 | 10 | 12 | 15 | 20 | 25 | 28 | 2. (d)

3. [grid with X]   4. 10 x 80 = 800   5. 175 cm

6. [dominoes]   7. answers vary   8. 7 out of 10

9. 60 mm line divided into 30 mm lengths

10. (d)   11. 234   12. 2 x 5 x 2

13. | 16 | 2 | 12 |
| 6 | 10 | 14 |
| 8 | 18 | 4 | 14. [hexagon]   15. 15 mm

Set 4 – Review

1. (d)   2. (c)   3. 12, 10

4. 36 marbles   5. D is 3x A   6. $58.00

7. [square diagram]   8. (c)   9. [clock]

10. 2 + 4 + 8   11. 600   12. 15 edges

13. square divided into 4 2-cm squares   14. 36

15. 100, 40

Set 5 – Review

1. (c)   2. (5 x 5) + 10 = 24 + 11

3. one number is 0   4. [dots]   5. B, C, D

6. 15, 21, 42, 99   7. 6.23 m, 2.07 m   8. (c)

9. [arrows]   10. HOT   11. $1

12. SOIL   13. [grid]   14. 36

15. 19 squares

Set 6 – Review

1. 5,012   2. (b)

3. | $10 | 5¢ | 20¢ | $5 | 50¢ | $2 | 10¢ | $1 | 4. [shape]

5. 4 vertices   6. 2,138   7. 500

8. 20 mm   9. 1,100   1,101   1,102

10. 50 mm   11. answers vary   12. 17 cm

13. F, E   14. IX XXI XII XVI VII XIV XV

15. 14 cubes

Set 7 – Review

1. 37,000   2. 22 x 6 = 11 x 12   3. $2\frac{1}{2}$, $1\frac{1}{2}$, $3\frac{1}{2}$

4. (b)   5. 19   6. 2.5 or $2\frac{1}{2}$

7. D   8. [shape] (6)   9. eight

10. (e)   11. [shape]   12. B and A

13. 9   14. 250 lots

15. [circles diagram] (answers vary)

Set 8 – Review

1. XXX   2. answers vary   3. even

4. AE12, AF14   5. [shapes]   6. answers vary

7. 8   2,768   3,020   1,084   8. (b)

9. Bob, Ann, Ian, Roy | 24 | 28 | 20 |
| 30 | 36 | 16 | 10. 500

11. (c)   12. | 40 | 12 | 60 | 13. 5

14. A, E, C, F   15. Amy $12, Ann $3, Toni $5

Set 9 – Review

1. [grid] 15   2. 742, smallest no. = 247

3. [clock]   4. 457   5. (c)

6. (d)   7. 18 cm²   8. $2\frac{1}{2}$ cm, 25 mm

9. John 8, Sue 16   10. (6 x 8) = 36 + 12

11. 4 + 1 = 2 + 3   12. 4 times   13. 21

14. 19 cm   15. Rose, Paul

Mental Math Workouts

Set 10 – Review

1. > (greater than) **2.** 10 **3.** C

4. odd **5.** answers vary **6.** door, brick, car

7. 5/8 **8.** (d)

9.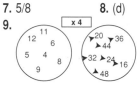

10. $2

11. (10 x 4) = 50 – 10

12.

13.
5 x Table	11 x Table	
5 25 15	11 33	Odd
10 30 20	22	Even

14. 2 cm, 20 mm

15. Mary, Pat, Jean, Alan

Set 11 – Review

1. (c) **2.**   **3.** = (equals)

4. 13:00 **5.** $^1/_{20}$, $^1/_4$, $^1/_2$ **6.** (d)

7. (c) **8.** C **9.**

10. 42 cubes **11.** Ann $15,

12.   Peta $10, Roy $5

13. 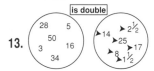 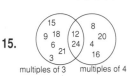 **15.**

multiples of 3   multiples of 4

14. 30

Set 12 – Review

1. 4 **2.** 4 **3.** (c)

4. 5,000+500+50+5 **5.**

6. (b) **7.** (c) **8.** $35

9. 14 fifties **10.** 7 cm or 70 mm **11.** (c)

12. outside, inside **13.** 9 **14.** odd, even

15.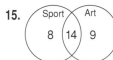